TALES FROM THE GREEK MYTHS

The Minotaur and the Labyrinth

Kostas Poulos
Illustrated by Sofia Papadopoulou

Translated by Leo Kalovyrnas

METAICHMIO

1st edition April 2018

ORIGINAL TITLE Κώστας Πούλος,
Λαβύρινθος και Μινώταυρος, Μεταίχμιο 2015

TRANSLATED FROM THE GREEK LANGUAGE BY Leo Kalovyrnas
ILLUSTRATED BY Sofia Papadopoulou

ISBN 978-618-03-1446-5
AUXIL. COMPU. CODE 81446
C.E.P. 4326 C.P. 9739

© 2017 METAICHMIO Publications
and Kostas Poulos

Bookstores
1. 18 ASKLIPIOU STR., 106 80 ATHENS
TEL. +30 210 3647433, FAX: +30 211 3003562
Internet Site: www.metaixmio.gr
e-mail: metaixmio@metaixmio.gr

2. POLYCHOROS, 118 IPPOKRATOUS STR., 114 72 ATHENS
TEL. +30 210 3003580, FAX: +30 211 3003581

This is so embarrassing. I can't even look you in the eye. I'm afraid of what you'll think of me when I tell you I'm the Minotaur. I know only too well what people say about me. It's in all the mythology books. According to the myth, I'm just a normal human being from my toes to my neck. My head, though, well, that's a wee bit different: it's the head of a bull. A man with a bull's head – what nonsense! It's a lie, but that's what everyone's been saying for years and years, so it's caught on. I almost believe it myself. One evening as I leaned over a lake to drink some water I saw my face.

entrance

find the way out

The truth is that I don't look like other people. But I am not a monster, no matter what the Athenians say! Because it's mostly them that speak ill of me and smear my name. They are the reason I've come to feel bad about myself. Even my father, King Minos, is ashamed of me, what with all the nasty talk going around about me. No wonder that eventually he locked me up in the palace basement. Now this basement is no ordinary cellar, it's absolutely huge, with an incredible amount of passageways – a proper labyrinth. If you're not familiar with the place, you may get lost forever. Needless to say, I know my way around like the palm of my hand. I can find the way out with my eyes shut.

But I don't want to.

Once upon a time...

I prefer my peace and quiet in here all alone rather than going out and be laughed at or get called a monster. It's just so unfair to be wronged like that. That's why now that I managed to muscle my way into this book, I'm going to tell you my story the way it really happened. So make yourself comfortable and listen to what I have to say.

I was born in Crete and I'm the son of a king. My father was King Minos, perhaps you've heard of him. He was no ordinary king, mind you. During his reign, Crete prospered and became the greatest kingdom. Everyone spoke of him with deep respect, also because he was the son of the god Zeus, and Europa.

Word is that it was Zeus himself who gave King Minos the laws with which he ruled this land with justice and fairness. My father turned Crete into a civilised country, and as long as he was King, life on the island was wonderful.

Knossos

During festivities we would play with bulls. Well, not everyone did, just the strongest and fastest lads. I was among them of course. Huge crowds would gather to witness the games. I would start by running next to the bull, then I'd grab him by the horns, hoist myself over him and plant my feet firmly on his back before doing a somersault and landing back on the ground.

I'm not one to brag, but I was the best at this sport. Which was a very dangerous sport, mind you. That's why spectators cheered and lavished praise on us. The true star, though, was the bull. Everyone in my country loved these animals. We worshipped them and wanted to be as noble and powerful as them. We even put on specially made bull masks with real horns during the festivities.

In loving memory of my son

Sporades

Dodecanese

Cyclades

Life on our island was just marvellous. Our Cretan ships plied the Mediterranean sea from one end to the other, bringing all sorts of delicacies to our land. Later, King Minos began his conquests and succeeded in holding sway over all the other islands. Then came Athens's turn.

My father absolutely detested the Athenians, and for very good reason! After all, it was in Athens that my brother Androgeus was murdered. Androgeus was a great athlete. One time he took part in an athletic contest in the city of Athens and beat all his opponents. But he never made it back to Crete. We got news that he was killed, but we never really found out exactly how or by whom. One thing's for certain, though: his death was an act of treachery, and it happened in Athens. King Minos got extremely angry and swore to avenge his son.

With his fleet and army he first enslaved the city of Megara and then Athens itself. Athenians were forced to pay tribute and taxes to us, but that was not enough; they had to send us young men and women as slaves. As a matter of fact, every seven years they were forced to send us seven lads and seven lasses, who worked as servants at our palace in Knossos. After all, our palace was huge, with over one thousand three hundred rooms, so you can imagine there was a lot of housework to be done. The palace store-rooms were in the cellars, and that's where we put the Athenian slaves to work, carrying wine and oil to the ewers. They weren't very happy about it, of course, but who can blame them? No one likes working like a slave.

cellar 20

cellar 21

cellar 19

7 lasses

7 lads

the throne

room 997

room 998

room 999

llar 19

Now the Athenians were fuming about this situation. No one wanted to see their children carried off to Crete as slaves. So they turned against their king Aegeus. 'How come our children get sent to Crete to be devoured by the Minotaur while you keep your own son Theseus safe and sound by your side? Send him instead!' they complained. So it was with grave heart that King Aegeus bade farewell to his son Theseus. A ship with pitch black sails and fourteen young men and women on board sailed off towards Crete. The king gave the ship's captain an order that if his son got through this alive and sailed back, the ship's black sails should be taken down and white ones should be hoisted, so that the good news could be seen from afar.

White is the colour of hope,
Black the colour of despair,
My fair ship, will you please
Bring my son back in one piece?

Theseus was a strapping young fellow, and was determined to take a brave stand against me. But if it wasn't for the help he got from my sister Ariadne, he would have utterly failed. It was Ariadne that gave him all the vital information, such as the fact that I slept in the labyrinth at night and that if he wanted to fight me, he'd need a sword. The most important piece of information, however, was that in order to get out of the labyrinth again, he would need a ball of thread. She made sure to supply him with everything he needed. My own flesh and blood advised Theseus on how to defeat me!

A sword and a ball of thread to lead you out of the maze

Ariadne

unravelling the thread

I wasn't sleeping heavily, I was dozing rather, when I heard his footsteps approaching. Theseus was unravelling Ariadne's ball of thread as he wove his way through the maze towards me. He knew that if he succeeded in defeating me, it would be like vanquishing the entire land of Crete. We got into a fight. Theseus was tough and brave. But I, too, was a real bull in strength and stamina – everybody said so.

There's no telling how long we wrestled in the darkness. It seemed like ages. Eventually he managed to defeat me sneakily by pulling a knife he had hidden in his clothes. He had bought that knife from a Cretan merchant.

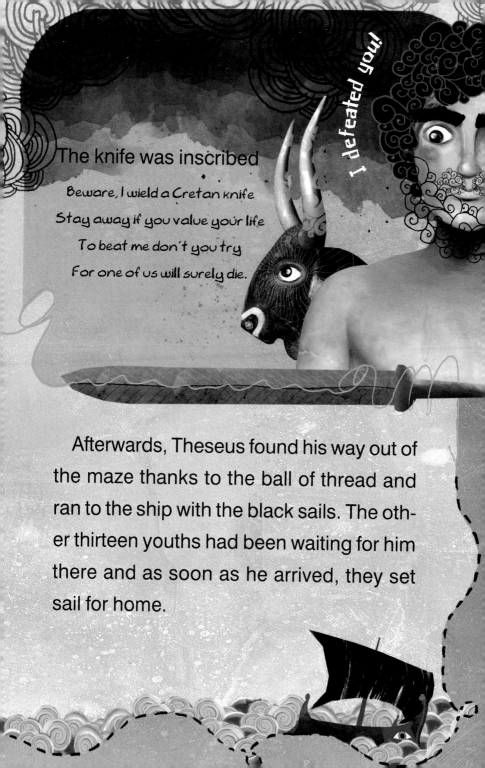

I defeated you!

The knife was inscribed

Beware, I wield a Cretan knife
Stay away if you value your life
To beat me don't you try
For one of us will surely die.

Afterwards, Theseus found his way out of the maze thanks to the ball of thread and ran to the ship with the black sails. The other thirteen youths had been waiting for him there and as soon as he arrived, they set sail for home.

They also took my sister with them, for Ariadne had fallen in love with Theseus, stupid girl that she was. She believed he'd make her his wife. But when they moored at the island of Naxos, Theseus abandoned

Theseus cut the thread that bound him to Ariadne

her there. Ariadne put a curse on him, and her curse came true soon enough, because the captain forgot to take down the black sails and hoist the white ones.

Back in Athens, days went by sorrowfully. Aegeus would sit high atop the cliffs of Sounio and gaze out at the sea, hoping to catch a glimpse of the returning white-sailed ship that would bring his son back. Then one day he caught sight of the raven-black sails far off. It was too much for him and he jumped off the cliff to his death in the sea that bears his name ever since: Aegean.

Read, look, and decide

So this is my story, the story of the Minotaur. To be perfectly honest, I'm a little confused myself. What am I really? Am I a man with the head of a bull or a 'monster' conjured by the imagination of the Athenians out of their fear for the mighty warriors of Crete? What do you think, reader of mine?

PLAYING
WITH THE
MYTH

Educational material
by Maria Gonidaki

THE MINOTAUR AND THE LABYRINTH

Minos, son of the god Zeus and princess Europa, was a great legendary king of Crete. King Minos had asked the god of the sea Poseidon to give him a divine sign in order to convince his siblings that he was the fittest to take the throne after the death of their mortal father. Poseidon obliged, and a magnificent bull rose out of the waves. Minos, however, forgot to sacrifice the bull to the god, so Poseidon decided to punish the king by making the king's wife, Pasiphaë fall in love with the bull. They mated, and she gave birth to the Minotaur, a double-natured monster. (Remember other similar creatures such as the Centaurs, the Sirens, or the Sphinx.) The Minotaur had the body of a man and the head of a bull.

King Minos got rid of the Minotaur by locking him up in the Labyrinth. This was a complex maze full of small chambers and lots of passageways built below the Knossos Palace by the renowned Athenian architect, sculptor and inventor Daedalus. No one had ever managed to find the way out of the Labyrinth. That is no one except for Theseus.

King Minos wanted to take revenge on the Athenians because he considered them responsible for the death of his son. He attacked Athens with his ships and asked Zeus to send a plague on the city of Athens. To put an end to all the suffering the Athenians agreed to send fourteen young men and women to Crete every seven years, where they were imprisoned in the Labyrinth. It was on one of these journeys that Theseus, the prince of Athens, sailed to Crete. With the help of the king's daughter Ariadne, Theseus managed to not only kill the Minotaur but also to find his way out of the maze thanks to a ball of thread which he unravelled as he went in. Then he set sail for Athens together with Ariadne and the other young men and women.

THE MINOAN CIVILISATION

The celebrated Minoan civilisation took its name after King Minos. The Minoan civilisation flourished from around 3000 BC to 1200 BC. Archaeological digs at various places in Crete have brought to light glorious palaces with great larders, and a lot of workshops where pottery, jewellery, stamps, and fabric were crafted. The Minoans cultivated the land, raised cattle, and were also extremely capable seamen, travelling across the Aegean all the way to Egypt, Cyprus, and the Middle East where they traded their produce for copper, silver, gold, and ivory.

▶ Take a look at the map and notice where the great big palaces of Minoan Crete were located.

• They are all near the coast. Why is that?

▶ Take a look at the layouts of the Cretan palaces. Do they look a bit like labyrinths?

KNOSSOS

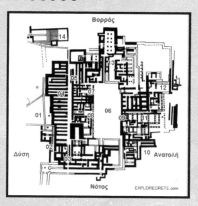

PHAISTOS

MALIA

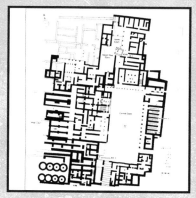

ZAKROS

WORD GAME

Fill in the missing words and the name of Minotaur's mother will appear vertically.

1. King Minos' mother.
2. Theseus's father.
3. The location of one of the magnificent palaces of Minoan Crete.
4. She helped Theseus defeat the Minotaur.
5. The Minoans built several of these across Crete.
6. What Theseus used to find his way out of the Labyrinth.
7. The architect of the Labyrinth.
8. The number of youths sent by Athens to Crete as slaves.

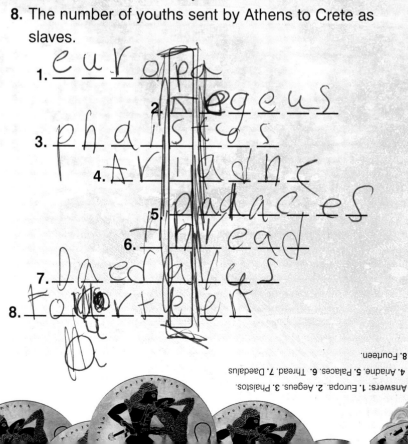

1. europa
2. aegeus
3. phaistos
4. Ariadne
5. palaces
6. thread
7. Daedalus
8. fourteen

▶ Take a look at the illustration on an ancient vase.

- Can you guess who the people shown there are?
- Write down their names in the blank spaces.
- Now take a closer look at their facial expressions. What kind of emotions did the ancient artist allow to show on the faces of the victor and the defeated?
- What's the role of the figure standing on the right?

. . . .

. . . .

▶ The fresco below is from the Palace at Knossos and it pictures an ancient ritual sport called Bull-leaping. This was a kind of sport during the Minoan era, related to the worship of bulls. The athletes would perform jumps, leaps, and other acrobatics over the bull without causing the animal any harm. That way they tried to show off how fearless and agile they were.

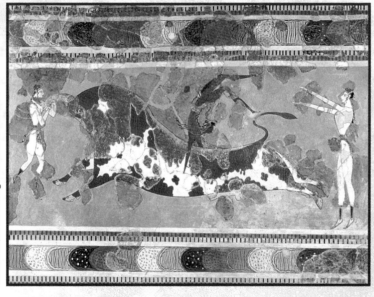

Heraklion, Archaeological Museum

▶ Take a look at the fresco and imagine what the entire scene of the ritual must have been like in the central courtyard of the palace.

- Who would be watching the ritual and where would they be sitting (e.g. the royal family and the aristocrats of Minoan society, the priests of Minoan religion, the people)?
- How did the spectators show their admiration for the competing athletes?
- Based on what criteria did the best athletes stand out? What prize do you think they got?

THINK ABOUT THIS...

Have you ever seen or heard about bullfighting in Spain?

What are the differences and similarities between Spanish bullfights and Minoan bull-leaping?

Sofia Papadopoulou

Sofia Papadopoulou lives and works in Athens, Greece. She studied Architecture at the National Technical University of Athens. After completing her studies, she began working professionally on children's book illustrations. She has worked with publishers such as Metaichmio, Kedros, Psichogios and Ocelotos. For the illustration of the book I'm telling you I'm not a monster, Kedros 2011, she was nominated for DIAVAZO magazine's awards. In January 2013 she exhibited her works as a solo artist in the 'Laspi Workshop' and has participated in various festivals. She was a student of the painter and sculptor Vasilis Katsivelakis, and is now being tutored by painter Pavlos Nikolakopoulos. Alongside her artistic work, she is a technical drawing instructor, preparing students for entering architectural and design faculties.

entrance

find the way out

**Kostas
Poulos**

Kostas Poulos was born in Elikonas, Viotia. He studied philology at the Universities of Athens, Würzburg, and Munich, and worked as a secondary school teacher both in Greece and abroad. He has written, translated and adapted several books for adults but chiefly for children for many publishing houses (Livanis, Boukoumanis, To Rodakio, Papadopoulos, Metaichmio). Some of his most famous books include: *Sun in the Garden*, *Half A Chocolate Is A Joke*, *One Ice-Cream Lasts Too Little*, *Nikos And The Wolf*, *Theofilos The Painter*, *Maria Callas*, *Scheherazade*, etc. His series of children's books The Greek Ones (Papadopoulos Publishers) includes classical texts of Greek literature from Homer to the present day especially adapted for kids. Poulos has also worked as a reader, editor, and reviewer for magazines and newspapers. His work has been translated into other languages and adapted for the theatre.

TALES FROM THE GREEK MYTHS
SERIES

Maria Angelidou

The Cattle of Geryon

Illustrated by
Iris Samartzi

METAICHMIO

TALES FROM THE GREEK MYTHS

Maria Angelidou

The Apples of the Hesperides

Illustrator:
Iris Samartzi

METAICHMIO

TALES FROM THE GREEK MYTHS

Maria Angelidou

The Girdle of Hippolyta

Illustrator:
Iris Samartzi

METAICHMIO

TALES FROM THE GREEK MYTHS

Maria Angelidou

The Capture of Cerberus

Illustrator:
Iris Samartzi

METAICHMIO

TALES FROM THE GREEK MYTHS

Maria Angelidou

The Lernaean Hydra

Illustrator:
Iris Samartzi

METAICHMIO

TALES FROM THE GREEK MYTHS

Maria Angelidou

The Stables of Augeas

Illustrator:
Iris Samartzi

METAICHMIO

TALES FROM THE GREEK MYTHS

Kostas Poulos

The Riddle of the Sphinx

Illustrator:
Sofia Papadopoulou

METAICHMIO

TALES FROM THE GREEK MYTHS

Kostas Poulos

The Song of the Sirens

Illustrator:
Sofia Papadopoulou

METAICHMIO

TALES FROM THE GREEK MYTHS